High-Frequency READERS™

I Am

Written by Adria Klein
Illustrated by Susan Gal

Scholastic Inc.
New York   Toronto   London   Auckland   Sydney
Mexico City   New Delhi   Hong Kong

No part of this publication may be reproduced in whole or in part, or stored in a retrieval system, or transmitted in any form or by any means, electronic, mechanical, photocopying, recording, or otherwise, without written permission of the publisher. For information regarding permission, write to: Permissions Department, Scholastic Inc., 557 Broadway, New York, NY 10012.

ISBN 0-439-13188-X

Copyright © 2000 by Scholastic Inc. All rights reserved. Published by Scholastic Inc.
SCHOLASTIC, HIGH-FREQUENCY READERS, and associated logos and designs are
trademarks and/or registered trademarks of Scholastic Inc.

12 11   5/0
                    Printed in China   62

I am running.

I am jumping.

I am building.

I am climbing.

I am dancing.

I am swinging.

I am sleeping.

HIGH-FREQUENCY WORDS

New	Review
am	I

High-Frequency READERS™

This edition is only
available for distribution through
the school market.

SCHOLASTIC INC.

0-439-13188-X